THE BEST OF THE BEATLES

BOOK 2

Wise Publications
London/New York/Sydney/Cologne

Exclusive Distributors:
Music Sales Limited
8/9 Frith Street, London W1V 5TZ, England.
Music Sales Pty. Limited
27 Clarendon Street, Artarmon, Sydney, NSW 2064, Australia.

This book © Copyright 1987 by
Wise Publications.
ISBN 0.7119.1178.9
UK Order No. NO 18558

Designed by Pearce Marchbank.
Cover Photography by Julian Hawkins.
Compiled by Peter Evans

Music Sales complete catalogue lists thousands of titles
and is free from your local music book shop,
or direct from Music Sales Limited.
Please send 50p in stamps for postage to:
Music Sales Limited, 8/9 Frith Street, London W1V 5TZ.

Printed in England by
J.B. Offset Printers (Marks Tey) Limited, Marks Tey.

THE SONGS

Help.

Words & Music: John Lennon and Paul McCartney.
© *Copyright 1966 Northern Songs, under licence to SBK Songs Limited, 3/5 Rathbone Place, London W1.*

Now I find   I've changed my mind,   I've o-pened up the doors. ___
I know that I   just need you like   I've nev - er done be-fore. ___
Help me if you

can. I'm feel-ing down _____   And I do ap - pre - ci-ate ___ you be-ing 'round. ___

Help me get ___ my feet back on the ground. _____

Won't you please,   please ___ help ___ me? ___

please ___ help ___ me? ___   Help   me!   Help   me! _____   Oo.

5

Another Girl.

Words & Music: John Lennon and Paul McCartney.

I've Just Seen A Face.

Words & Music: John Lennon and Paul McCartney.

1. I've just seen a face, I can't for- get the time or place where we just met, she's just the girl for me and I want all the world to see we've met.

2. Had it been an- oth- er day I might have looked the oth- er way and I'd have nev- er been a- ware but as it is I'll dream of her to- night.

3. I have nev- er known the like of this, I've been a- lone and I have missed things and kept out of sight for oth- er girls were nev- er quite like this.

Mm mm mm mm mm mm.
Da da da da da da.
Mm mm mm mm mm mm.

Fall- ing,_ Yes, I am fall- ing,_ And she keeps call- ing_ me back a- gain. _____ gain. _____

Tell Me What You See.

Words & Music: John Lennon and Paul McCartney.
© Copyright 1966 Northern Songs, under licence to SBK Songs Limited, 3/5 Rathbone Place, London W1.

Tell me what you see_____

solo

Coda

D.S. %

mm mm

mm mm mm

solo

Ticket to Ride.

Words & Music: John Lennon and Paul McCartney.

She's got a tick-et to ride____ but she don't care.____ 2. She

I don't know why she's rid-ing so high,____ She ought to

think right, she ought to do right by me. Be-fore she gets to say-ing good-bye,____

She ought to think right, she ought to do right by me. 3. She

My ba-by don't care. My ba-by don't

Repeat and fade

Yesterday.

Words & Music: John Lennon and Paul McCartney.
© *Copyright 1966 Northern Songs, under licence to SBK Songs Limited, 3/5 Rathbone Place, London W1.*
All rights reserved. International copyright secured.

Moderato

Yes-ter-day,

Em7   A7   Dm   Dm/C bass   Bb   C7

all my trou-bles seemed so far a-way   Now it looks as though they're

F   C   Dm   G   Bb   F

here to stay__ Oh I be-lieve__ in yes-ter-day.__ Sud-den-ly

Em7   A7   Dm   Dm/C bass   Bb   C7

I'm not half the man I used to be   There's a shad-ow hang-ing

You've Got To Hide Your Love Away.

Words & Music: John Lennon and Paul McCartney.
© *Copyright 1966 Northern Songs, under licence to SBK Songs Limited, 3/5 Rathbone Place, London W1.*
All rights reserved. International copyright secured.

I'm Looking Through You.

Words & Music: John Lennon and Paul McCartney.

I'm Look-ing Through You_ you're not_ the same.
I'm Look-ing Through You_ you're not_ the same.

Why, tell me

why did you not treat me right?_ Love has a

nas-ty hab-it of dis-ap-pear-ing o-ver-night. You're think-ing

of me ___ in the same old way. You were a-

bove me ___ but not to - day. The on - ly

dif - f'rence ___ is you're down there. I'm Look - ing Through You ___

and you're ___ no - where.

Repeat and fade

You Won't See Me.

Words & Music: John Lennon and Paul McCartney.
© Copyright 1966 Northern Songs, under licence to SBK Songs Limited, 3/5 Rathbone Place, London W1.

Drive My Car.

Words & Music: John Lennon and Paul McCartney.

In My Life.

Words & Music: John Lennon and Paul McCartney.

still can re-call.___ Some are dead___ and___ some___ are___ liv-ing, In my___ life I've
went___ be-fore.___ I know I'll of - ten stop and think a -bout them, In my___ life I'll

loved them all.___
love you more.___
2. But of

Though I
know___ I'll___ nev-er lose af-fec-tion for peo-ple and things___ that went be-fore___ I

know I'll of - ten stop and think a -bout them, In my___ life I'll love you more.___

ten.
In my___ life I'll love you more.

27

Norwegian Wood.

Words & Music: John Lennon and Paul McCartney.
© *Copyright 1966 Northern Songs, under licence to SBK Songs Limited, 3/5 Rathbone Place, London W1.*
All rights reserved. International copyright secured.

Run For Your Life.

Words & Music: John Lennon and Paul McCartney.
© Copyright 1966 Northern Songs, under licence to SBK Songs Limited, 3/5 Rathbone Place, London W1.
All rights reserved. International copyright secured.

Medium Beat

Well I'd rath - er see you dead ___ lit - tle girl than to be with an - oth - er man ___
know that I'm a wick - ed guy and I was born with a jeal - ous mind ___

You'd bet - ter keep your head ___ lit - tle girl or I
And I can't spend my whole ___ life try - in' just to

won't know where I am ___ You'd bet - ter run for your life if you can ___
make you toe the line ___

lit - tle girl___ Hide your head___ in the sand___ lit - tle girl___

Am   F   E7   Am

Catch you with an - oth - er man___ that's the end___ a lit - tle

C7

girl.

1.2.3.   4.

Well you   No no no___   No no no___

Repeat and fade

Nowhere Man.

Words & Music: John Lennon and Paul McCartney.

please lis-ten, ____ You don't know ____ what you're miss-ing, ____ No-where Man. ___
don't wor-ry, ____ Take your time, _____ Don't hur-ry, _ Leave it all __

The world _____ is at your com-mand.
till some-bod-y else _____ lends you a hand.

Coda

Mak-ing all __ his no-where plans __ for no - bod - y.

Mak-ing all __ his no-where plans __ for no-bod-y.

rit.

Eleanor Rigby.

Words & Music: John Lennon and Paul McCartney.

Moderately, with a steady beat

lower notes optional

Ah _____ look at all __ the lone - ly peo - ple! _____

Ah _____ look at all __ the lone - ly peo - ple! _____

1. E - lea - nor Rig - by,   picks up the rice ___ in the church where a wed - ding has been,
2. Fath - er Mc Ken - zie,   writ - ing the words ___ of a ser - mon that no - one will hear,
3. E - lea - nor Rig - by,   died in the church ___ and was bur - ied a - long ___ with her name,

lives in a dream. _____   Waits at the win - dow,
no one comes near. _____ 'Look at him work - ing,
no - bod - y came. _____   Fa - ther Mc ken - zie,

34

wear - ing the face ___ that she keeps ___ in a jar ___ by the door, _____
darn - ing his socks ___ in the night ___ when there's no - bod - y there, _____
wip - ing the dirt ___ from his hands ___ as he walks ___ from the grave, _____

who is it for? ___
what does he care? ___ } All the lone - ly peo - ple, where do ___ they all ___ come from? ___
no one was saved. ___

All the lone - ly peo - ple, where do ___ they all ___ be - long? ___

To Coda

1. | 2.

D.C. al
Coda

Go to beginning

Coda

35

Here There And Everywhere.

Words & Music: John Lennon and Paul McCartney.

For No One.

Words & Music: John Lennon and Paul McCartney.
© Copyright 1966 Northern Songs, under licence to SBK Songs Limited, 3/5 Rathbone Place, London W1.
All rights reserved. International copyright secured.

Your day___ breaks your mind___ aches you find___ that all___
She wakes___ up she makes___ up she takes___ her time___

___ her words of kind - ness lin - ger on___ when she no
___ and does - n't feel she has to hur - ry she no

long - er needs___ you___   And in her
long - er needs___ you___

eyes you see noth - ing___   no sign of

38

Bb   C   to Coda ✛ 1.   2.
                                                        D.S. 𝄋 al Coda ✛

___ is dead you think she needs___ you ___ And in her ___
___ he's gone she does-n't need___ him ___
___ your head you won't for - get___ her___

Coda ✛ C   Dm   A7

___ And in her eyes   you   see   noth-ing_____

Dm   A7   Dm   A7

no sign of love be-hind the tears___   cried for no___ one

Dm   A7   Dm   G7sus4 G7

a   love   that   should have   last - ed   years.___

rit.

40

She Said She Said.

Words & Music: John Lennon and Paul McCartney.

Moderato

She said _____ I know what it's like to be dead
I said _____ who put all those things in your hair

I know what it is to be sad And she's
Things that make me feel that I'm mad And you're

mak-ing me feel_ like I've nev-er been born_
mak-ing me feel_ like I've nev-er been born_

I know that I'm read-y to leave   'Cos you're

mak-ing me feel like I've nev-er been born

She said   She said   I know what it's like to be dead   I know what it's

like to be dead   I know what it   is to be sad   I know what it is to be sad   I know what it

Repeat and fade

43

Good Day Sunshine.

Words & Music: John Lennon and Paul McCartney.
© Copyright 1966 Northern Songs, under licence to SBK Songs Limited, 3/5 Rathbone Place, London W1.

Got To Get You Into My Life.

Words & Music: John Lennon and Paul McCartney.
© Copyright 1966 Northern Songs, under licence to SBK Songs Limited, 3/5 Rathbone Place, London W1.

ev - 'ry sin - gle day of my life? _____
say we'll be to - geth - er ev - 'ry day. _____
ev - 'ry sin - gle day of my life? _____

(Shout)
Got to get you in - to my life! _____

(Solo)

To Coda ⊕

D. S. al ⊕ Coda

Coda
(No Chords)

Got to get you in - to my life! __

D. C. and fade after 4 bars.